HOPSCOTCH
STORIES OF
RELIGION

The Loaves
and the Fishes

First published in 2008 by
Franklin Watts
338 Euston Road
London
NW1 3BH

Franklin Watts Australia
Level 17/207 Kent Street
Sydney
NSW 2000

A CIP catalogue record for this book is available
from the British Library.

ISBN 978 0 7496 8370 2 (hbk)
ISBN 978 0 7496 8376 4 (pbk)

Series Editor: Melanie Palmer
Series Advisor: Dr Barrie Wade
Series Designer: Peter Scoulding

Printed in China

Franklin Watts is a division of
Hachette Children's Books,
an Hachette Livre UK company
www.hachettelivre.co.uk

The Loaves
and the Fishes

by Anita Ganeri and Natascia Ugliano

W
FRANKLIN WATTS
LONDON•SYDNEY

About this book

The story of the Loaves and the Fishes comes from the Bible. The Bible is the name that Christians give to their holy book. They believe that the Bible is the word of God and that it teaches people how God wants them to live and behave. The Bible is divided into two parts, called the Old Testament and the New Testament. The Loaves and the Fishes is found in the Gospels of Matthew (chapter 14; verses 15-21), Mark (chapter 6; verses 35-44), Luke (chapter 9; verses 12-17), and John (chapter 6; verses 5-13). In the story, through the power of God, Jesus performs a miracle and provides food for a huge number of people.

One afternoon, Jesus was out
with his friends, the disciples.

Jesus had spent all day by
a lake, teaching the huge
crowds about God.

People came from far away
because they wanted to hear
him speak.

"Come," said Jesus to his friends.
"We'll take a boat across the lake
and find a quiet place to rest."

The disciples cheered. They were looking forward to getting away and having a break.

But when they reached the other
side of the lake, thousands of
people were standing there.

They had heard that Jesus was
coming and had waited all day
to see him.

"Please send them away, Jesus," the disciples begged. "It's getting late and everyone is tired."

But Jesus did not listen. He called
to the crowd to come closer and
began talking to them.

As the afternoon turned into evening, the disciples came up to Jesus again.

"Send them away, Master," they said. "It's late and everyone is getting hungry."

"Then you must find them
something to eat," Jesus told them.

"But there are thousands of people here," Philip, one of the disciples, said. "We can't feed them all!"

Just then, another disciple, Andrew,
came over. He had a small boy
with him, carrying a basket.

"You can have my food,"
the boy said to Jesus and he
handed over the basket.

The disciples looked in the basket and saw just two small fishes and five bread rolls. How could that feed thousands of people?

But Jesus turned to the boy.
"Thank you," he said, smiling.

"Put the people into groups,"
Jesus told the disciples. "And tell
everybody to sit down."

Jesus held up the food in his hands and thanked God for it.

Then he took the five rolls and two fishes and broke them into pieces.

He gave the pieces to the disciples
to share out among the groups.

There was more than enough
food for everyone! The disciples
were amazed.

However fast they shared the food out, Jesus always had more to give to them.

Soon everyone was full up on the fish and bread. Then people began to make their way back home.

"Go and collect up the leftovers," Jesus told the disciples. "So that nothing is wasted."

There was so much food left over
that the disciples filled twelve big
baskets.

Then, at last, the disciples got a well-earned rest and a delicious meal to eat.

Hopscotch has been specially designed to fit the requirements of the Literacy Framework. It offers real books by top authors and illustrators for children developing their reading skills.

* hardback